Easter Celebration

AN EASTER CANTATA by
Harold DeCou

 SINGSPIRATION MUSIC
OF THE ZONDERVAN CORPORATION
GRAND RAPIDS, MICHIGAN 49506

The following supplemental material is available for this musical:

Bulletin Covers	4313B
Full Orchestration	4313V
Brass Ensemble	4313E
Music/Record Combination	4313C
Instrumental Tape Track	4313T

7½ IPS reel to reel

Stereo Record Album	ZLP964S
8-Track Cartridge Tape	ZLT964S
Cassette	ZLC964S

Easter Celebration

Words and Music by
HAROLD DeCOU

vic - tor-y _____ to con-quer sin. Such love be -

yond de-gree _____ He showed at Cal - va-ry _____ To pay the

pen - al - ty _____ for sin-ners such as we; Eas-ter cel - e -

bra-tion _____ tells us of sal-va-tion, For it tells of

Christ who came _____ our souls to win— Eas-ter cel-e-

molto rall.

bra-tion! Eas-ter cel-e-bra-tion! _____

sit

TENOR SOLO
mp **Earnestly, rather freely**

Why did Je-sus come to earth, Leav-ing heav'n with all its worth? Why a low-ly hum-ble birth? For you, for me! Why did He temp-ta-tion know When He lived here long a-go? This ex-am-ple He did show— For you, for me!

SOPRANO SOLO

mp *Earnestly, rather freely*

Can you now the time re-call Je-sus stood in Pi-late's hall?

alter Sw. *mp*

There con-demned by one and all— For you, for me!

Do you know and have you heard That He did not speak a word

When men's in-sults He in-curred For you, for me?

Gt.

DUET

With deep feeling, in a steady tempo

For you, for me —— the Sav-ior came, Good news to all —— He did pro-claim; For you, for me —— He bore sin's shame, For you, for me —— the Sav-ior came.

Organ l.h. may assist in treble clef

* Throughout the cantata, the symbol ⑤ will instruct the organist to sustain the initial chord while the pianist progresses through the inversions or arpeggios of the chord.

shame, For you, for me _____ the Sav-ior came, _____

For you, for me the Sav - ior came. _____

★ *NARRATOR:* Many people . . . when they heard that Jesus was coming to Jerusalem, took branches of palm trees, and went forth to meet him. (*John 12:12-13a*)

bring. _____ They shout-ed their loud ac - cla - ma-tions, ___ The
jeer. _____ But now they are anx-ious to see Him, ___ They'd

MEN in unison *mf* *Very rhythmically*

palm-branch-es strewed in the way; ___ With an - tic - i - pa-tion and
heard of His won - der-ful ways; ___ They looked for a glo-rious and

fran - tic ex - cite-ment They wel-comed the King on that day. _____
bright new day dawn-ing— How joy-ous their pae - an of praise! ___

* John 1:11-12

★ *NARRATOR:* All the chief priests and elders of the people took counsel against Jesus to put him to death; And when they had bound him, they led him away, and delivered him to Pontius Pilate the governor. (*Matthew 27:1-2*)

MEDIUM VOICE SOLO

*Je - sus is stand - ing in Pi - late's hall—

Friend - less, for - sak - en, be - trayed by all:

Hark - en! what mean - eth the sud - den call!

What will you do with Je - sus?_____

* WHAT WILL YOU DO WITH JESUS?—text by Albert B. Simpson.

What will you do with Je - sus? Neu-tral you can - not be; _____ Some day your heart will be ask - ing, "What will He do with me?" _____

26

CHOIR

SOLO, continued

Will you, like Pe - ter, your Lord de - ny?

Or will you scorn from His foes to fly,

Dar - ing for Je - sus to live or die?

What will you do with Je - sus?

★ *NARRATOR:* Then Pilate delivered him unto them to be crucified. And they took Jesus, and led him away. And when they were come to the place which is called Calvary, there they crucified him. (*John 19:16, Luke 23:33a*)

CHOIR
Rather slowly, with a sense of awe

On a hill called Cal-va-ry

Je - sus suf - fered will-ing-ly, Then in un - told

ag - o - ny   His own life He   gave;   There He won the
gave, He gave;

vic - to - ry,   There   He bought our lib - er - ty,

There He paid sin's pen - al - ty   This lost world to save.

32

Full Choir
Broadly

We like sheep have gone a-stray, We have turned to our own way, And the Lord on Him did lay All our sin and shame; (shame, our shame;) Let us thank Him for that day

HIGH VOICE SOLO

1. Up - on that tree ——— my eye can see ——— The dy-ing form of Christ the
2. What love He showed,——— on me be-stowed, ——— That day He gave His life on

cru - ci - fied; It was for me—— how can it be ——— That through His
Cal - va - ry! A-mazed am I ——— that He would buy ——— A par - don

sac - ri - fice I'm jus - ti - fied?
for my sin and set me free.

It was God's will,

it was God's plan That His own Son ——— should die for man;

★*NARRATOR:* In the end of the sabbath, as it began to dawn toward the first day of the week, came Mary Magdalene and the other Mary to see the sepulchre. And when they looked, they saw that the stone was rolled away. And it came to pass, as they were much perplexed thereabout, behold, two men stood by them in shining garments ... and said unto them, Why seek ye the living among the dead? He is not here, but is risen. (*Matthew 28:1, Mark 16:4, Luke 24: 4-6*)

Al - le - lu - ia, al - le - lu! See the place where Je - sus lay;
Al - le - lu - ia, al - le - lu! Christ the Lord is

38

ris'n to - day! Look in - side the emp-ty tomb,

MEN f.

Gone three days of dread-ful gloom.

WOMEN in unison
mf

Al - le - lu - ia,

al - le - lu! See the place where Je - sus lay;

39

He is ris-en as He said. He has con-quered death and

sin, He the vic-to-ry did win!

MEN in unison

Al - le-lu - ia, al - le - lu! He is ris-en from the dead;

Christ the Lord is ris'n to-day! Lift your voice and with us

sing, Lives a - gain our glo - rious King!

Al - le - lu - ia, al - le - lu! Let us cel - e - brate this day,

Al - le - lu - ia, al - le - lu! Christ the Lord is ris'n to-day!

Ris'n to-day! Christ the Lord is

Ris'n to-day!

ris'n to - day!

DUET

With deep feeling, in a steady tempo

For you, for me — the Sav-ior came, Good news to all — He did pro-claim; For you, for me — He bore sin's shame, For you, for

MEDIUM VOICE SOLO

Entreatingly, in a moderate tempo

shame;
shame, our shame; Let us thank Him for that day

When He washed our sin a-way— What a price He

had to pay Man-kind to re-claim!

HIGH VOICE SOLO
With conviction

It was God's will, it was God's plan That His own Son — should die for man; What can I say? what can I do? My life I give, Lord, my love I give, Lord; My life, my love, Lord, I give to You. —

CHOIR

Brightly

Al - le - lu - ia, al - le - lu! Let us cel - e -

brate this day, Al - le - lu - ia, al - le - lu! Christ the

Lord is ris'n to - day! Lift your voice and with us sing,

Lives a - gain our glo-rious King! Al - le - lu - ia,

al - le - lu! Let us cel - e - brate this day,

Al - le - lu - ia, al - le - lu! Christ the Lord is

come   the   sons   of   God;   But   as   man - y

as   re - ceived him, _____   as   man - y   as   re-

ceived him, _____   to   them   gave   he   pow'r........

NARRATOR: (*without music*) All this is written that ye might believe that Jesus is the Chris
the Son of God; and that believing ye might have life through his name. (*John 20:31*)

Eas-ter cel - e - bra-tion _____ tells us of sal - va-tion,

For it tells of Christ who came _____ our souls to win;

By His life He taught us, _____ through His death He bought us,

And He rose in vic - to - ry _____ to con-quer sin.

Smoothly
mf unison

Such love be - yond de-gree ____ He showed at Cal - va-ry ____ To pay the

unison

Sw.
mf

8va

With the use of "artificial banding," the recording (ZLP-964S) of EASTER CELEBRATION provides the choir director, accompanist, or choir member with the maximum assistance in locating various segments of the cantata as indicated below:

SIDE ONE

SIDE TWO